Grades K-4

Focus On Elementary

Teacher's Manual

3rd Edition

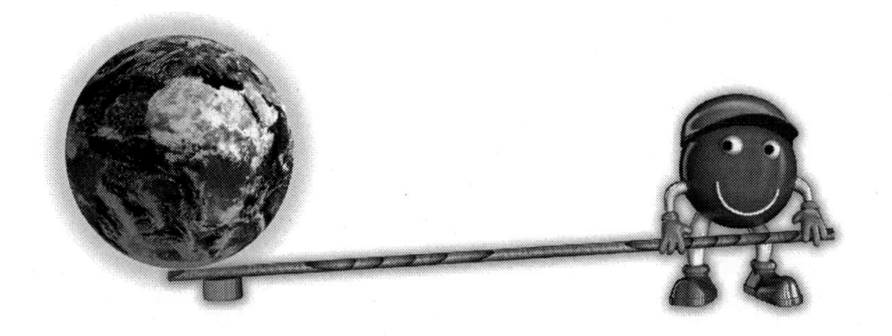

Rebecca W. Keller, PhD

Real Science-4-Kids

Illustrations: Janet Moneymaker

Focus On Elementary Physics Teacher's Manual—3rd Edition
ISBN 978-1-941181-44-7

Published by Gravitas Publications Inc.
www.gravitaspublications.com
www.realscience4kids.com

A Note From the Author

This curriculum is designed to provide an introduction to physics for students in the elementary level grades. *Focus On Elementary Physics—3rd Edition* is intended to be used as the first step in developing a framework for the study of real scientific concepts and terminology in physics. This *Teacher's Manual* will help you guide students through the series of experiments in the *Laboratory Notebook*. These experiments will help the students develop the skills needed for the first step in the scientific method — making good observations.

There are several sections in each chapter. The section called *Observe It* helps the students explore how to make good observations. The *Think About It* section provides questions for the students to think about and use to make further observations. In every chapter there is a *What Did You Discover?* section that gives the students an opportunity to summarize the observations they have made. A section called *Why?* provides a short explanation of what students may or may not have observed. And finally, in each chapter there is a section called *Just For Fun* that contains an additional activity.

The experiments take up to 1 hour. The materials needed for each experiment are listed on the next page and also at the beginning of each experiment.

Enjoy!

Rebecca W. Keller, PhD

Materials at a Glance

Experiment 1	Experiment 3	Experiment 4	Experiment 5	Experiment 6
2 tennis balls other objects such as: apple orange rubber ball cotton ball or feather **Experiment 2** clock or stopwatch	large marshmallow tennis ball objects such as: rubber ball lemon or lime rock banana pliers	toy car stiff cardboard or board (approximately .3 meter wide x 1 meter long [1 foot x 3 feet]) several marshmallows **Optional** pennies tape	2 marbles 3 playing cards shallow jar top vinegar baking soda measuring spoons **Suggested** dominoes blocks electric car electric train marshmallow tongue depressor steel ball other objects chosen by the student	1 small glass marble 1 large glass marble

Experiment 7	Experiment 8	Experiment 9	Experiment 10	Experiment 11
stopwatch or clock an area to run in items for marking the beginning and ending of the running distance	4 plastic or Styrofoam cups with the mouth larger than the base 2 long poles (dowels work well or any two long sticks that are the same thickness from end to end) tape a cylinder, 10-13 cm long (4-5 inches) [any cylindrical object, such as a pencil, a dowel, a cylindrical block, or a cylindrical drinking glass that is not tapered; a paper towel tube may be used if it is filled with sand and the ends taped] chalk	3-5 large lemons knife 3-5 copper pennies older than 1982 3-5 galvanized (zinc coated) nails LED (recommended: 20mA 2 pin LED bulb, any color)* 4-6 pairs alligator clips [duct tape can be substituted for alligator clips] plastic coated copper wire, .6-1.2 m (2-4 feet) wire clippers small Phillips screwdriver	2-3 rubber balloons string or thread, at least 2 meters (6 feet) cut in half scissors different materials to rub the balloon on, such as: cotton clothing silk clothing wool clothing wooden surface plaster wall metal surface leather surface	lemon battery supplies (see *Lemon Energy* experiment) suggested test materials: Styrofoam plastic block cotton ball nickel coin metal paperclip plastic paperclip glass of water table salt, 15 ml (1 Tbsp.) **Experiment 12** two bar magnets with the poles labeled "N" and "S"

* A browser search can be used to look for an electronic parts store in your area. Or you can search on "20mA LED bulb 2 pin" to find an online supplier. An LED with flexible pins may be easier to use.
It should look something like this:

Materials: Quantities Needed for All Experiments

Equipment

alligator clips, 4-6 pairs [duct tape can be substituted for alligator clips]
ball, rubber
balls, tennis, 2
clock or stopwatch
cylinder, 10-13 cm long (4-5 inches) [such as a pencil, a dowel, a cylindrical block, or a cylindrical drinking glass that is not tapered; a paper towel tube may be used if it is filled with sand and the ends taped]
jar top, shallow
knife
magnets, bar, 2, with the poles labeled "N" and "S"
marble, glass, small
marble, glass, large
marbles, 2
measuring spoons
pennies, 3-5 copper, older than 1982
playing cards, 3
pliers
poles, 2 long (dowels or any two long sticks that are the same thickness from end to end)
scissors
screwdriver, small Phillips
toy car
wire clippers

Optional

pennies

Suggested

ball, steel
blocks
car, electric
coin, nickel
dominoes
train, electric

Materials

balloons, 2-3 rubber
cardboard, stiff, or board (approx .3 meter wide x 1 meter long [1 foot x 3 feet])
chalk
cotton balls
cups, 4 plastic or Styrofoam with the mouth larger than the base
feather
items for marking the beginning and ending of a running distance
LED (recommended: 20mA 2 pin LED bulb, any color)*
materials, misc., to rub a balloon on, such as:
- cotton clothing
- silk clothing
- wool clothing
- wooden surface
- plaster wall
- metal surface
- leather surface

nails, 3-5 galvanized (zinc coated)
objects, misc.
rock
string or thread, at least 2 meters (6 feet) cut in half
tape
wire, copper, plastic coated, .6-1.2 m (2-4 feet) or more

Suggested Test Materials:

paperclip, metal
paperclip, plastic
Styrofoam, 1 piece
table salt, 15 ml (1 Tbsp.)
tongue depressor

Foods

apple
baking soda
banana
lemon, 6-10 large
lemon or lime
marshmallow, large, several
orange
vinegar

Other

an area to run in

* A browser search can be used to look for an electronic parts store in your area. Or you can search on "20mA LED bulb 2 pin" to find an online supplier. An LED with flexible pins may be easier to use.
It should look something like this:

Contents

Experiment 1

Falling Objects

Materials Needed

- 2 tennis balls
- other objects such as:
  apple
  orange
  rubber ball
  cotton ball or feather

Objectives

In this experiment students will try to determine if Galileo was right.

The objectives of this lesson are to have students:

- Compare their own observations with a scientific discovery.
- Compare different observations.

Experiment

I. Observe It

In this section students will observe how two objects fall when they are released at the same time.

Read this section of the *Laboratory Notebook* with your students.

❶ Have the students hold a tennis ball in each hand with their arms outstretched at chest level.

❷ Have the students release the two tennis balls at the same time.

❸ Help them observe how the objects land on the ground. Guide their inquiry with the following questions.

- *Did both objects land at the same time?*
- *Is one object heavier or lighter than the other object?*
- *Do you think it matters how high you hold the objects? Why or why not?*
- *Do you think the shape of the object matters? Why or why not?*

❹ Help the students record their observations in the *Observe It* section of their *Laboratory Notebook* (see example on next page).

❺ Have the students repeat the experiment using different combinations of objects. Have them compare at least four different pairs of objects. For each set of objects, help the students record their observations in the boxes provided.

In the spaces next to **Object 1** and **Object 2**, have the students write the names of the objects they will be dropping. Then have them draw or write a description of what they see. Help them make good observations by asking questions such as:

- *How heavy does Object 1 feel in your hand?*
- *How heavy does Object 2 feel in your hand?*
- *Does Object 1 feel heavier or lighter in your hand than Object 2?*
- *Is it easy to release both objects at the same time? Why or why not?*
- *Describe the shape of Object 1.*
- *Describe the shape of Object 2.*

Object 1 *apple*

Object 2 *tennis ball*

(Answers will vary.)

The apple feels heavier in my hand than the tennis ball.

When I drop the objects, I have a hard time seeing which one lands first. They look like they land together, but I am not sure.

I can release the objects at the same time from my hands.

The apple is a different shape than the tennis ball, but they still land at the same time.

II. Think About It

Read the questions with your students.

❶ Have the students think about their experiment and make observations about how easy or difficult it was to determine if the objects fell at the same speed.

- *Could you see the objects fall to the floor?*
- *Could you determine if both objects hit the floor at the same time?*
- *Was it easy or difficult to release the objects from both hands at the same time?*

❷ Help the students think about ways to vary their experiment.

- *If they can't see the objects fall to the floor, maybe they can get a parent, sibling, or friend to make the observations.*
- *Could they use a mirror to more easily see the objects hit the floor?*
- *What would happen if the objects were dropped from a greater height? Students could stand on a sturdy chair or bench to see if greater height makes a difference.*
- *What would happen if the objects were dropped from a lower height? Students could release the objects at waist or knee height.*

❸ Help the students repeat the experiment for one of their object pairs. Have them vary only one parameter at a time for one set of objects. For example, they may want to hold the objects higher and have a friend observe how they fall. But this is changing two parameters (the height and the observer), and if the results varied, the students couldn't tell which change to the experiment brought about the variation. Explain to them that scientists try to change only one parameter at a time so that they can make comparisons to previous experiments, noting what difference, if any, changing that one parameter had on the experimental results.

❹ Help the students record their observations.

III. What Did You Discover?

Read the questions with your students.

❶-❹ The questions can be answered verbally or in writing. With these questions help the students think about their observations. There are no right answers to these questions, and it is important for the students to write or discuss what they actually observed.

IV. Why?

Read this section of the *Laboratory Notebook* with your students.

Help the students understand that two objects of different weights will fall to Earth at the same speed. Both objects have the same amount of gravity pulling on them at the same time, so both objects start with the same force. Because both objects have the same force, they will both fall to the Earth at the same speed since the speed of an object is independent of its weight.

V. Just For Fun

Read this section of the *Laboratory Notebook* with your students.

The students can try an experiment with an object that is much lighter than the objects they have been using. A cotton ball or a feather would work. They will discover that if an object is too light, it will float to the ground and not fall at the same time as a heavier object. However, tell them that if the two objects are put in a vacuum, they will fall at the same time. Even an apple and a feather or cotton ball will fall at the same time. In a vacuum there is no air resistance. Outside the vacuum, the air pushes up on the cotton ball, and because the cotton ball is light enough, the air will slow it down.

Experiment 2

Measuring Time

Materials Needed

- Clock or stopwatch

Objectives

In this experiment, students will explore how to use a basic tool to measure an important physics parameter— time.

The objectives of this lesson are for students to:

- Use suitable tools, techniques, and quantitative measurements when appropriate.
- Use a simple tool to make measurements.

Experiment

I. Think About It

Read this section of the *Laboratory Notebook* with your students.

Have the students think about different events they could measure. Use questions such as the following to explore open inquiry and suggest possible events to measure.

- *How long does it take you to go to school, to the grocery store, or to a park or museum?*
- *How long does it take you to brush your teeth?*
- *How long does it take you to eat breakfast?*
- *How long does it take you to walk around your house?*
- *How long does it take you to ride your bike down the block?*
- *How long does it take your mom or dad to walk the length of your backyard?*

Guide the students in coming up with 3 events they would like to measure and have them write these down. The instructions require that they time each event twice, so help them pick events they can measure more than once.

II. Observe It

Read this section of the *Laboratory Notebook* with your students.

Help the students use the clock or stopwatch. Have them record the time for an event and then repeat the event and record the time again. Make sure they record both the start time and end time. Then help them calculate the length of time for each occurrence.

Have them record any other observations they think are important or interesting. A box is provided for each event.

III. What Did You Discover?

Read this section of the *Laboratory Notebook* with your students.

❶-❻ Have the students answer the questions. These can be answered orally or in writing. There are no right answers and their answers will depend on what they actually observed.

IV. Why?

Read this section of the *Laboratory Notebook* with your students.

Discuss any questions that might come up.

V. Just For Fun

Have the students mark a distance they can run. Then have them measure how fast they can run that given distance. Have them repeat several times, recording the time it takes for each round and any other observations they find important or interesting. They can use a timer themselves or have someone else do it for them.

Experiment 3

Get To Work!

Materials Needed

- large marshmallow
- tennis ball
- objects such as:
  rubber ball
  lemon or lime
  rock
  banana
- pliers

Objectives

In this experiment students will explore the concept that work happens when energy is used to create a force that moves an object, changes its shape, or changes its velocity.

The objectives of this lesson are for students to:

- Explore the concepts of work, force, and energy.
- Make careful observations.

Experiment

I. Observe It

In this part of the experiment students will apply a force to different objects and compare the results.

Read this section of the *Laboratory Notebook* with your students.

❶ Have the students observe a marshmallow. Have them write or draw a description of the size, shape, and color of the marshmallow in the "Before" section section of their *Laboratory Notebook* (see example on following page).

❷-❹ Have the students hold the marshmallow in one hand and then press the marshmallow with the palm and fingers of their hand. Use the following questions to help the students observe how much effort they used while squeezing the marshmallow.

- *Was it easy or difficult to squeeze the marshmallow?*
- *Were you able to squeeze the marshmallow completely? Why or why not?*
- *Would you describe the marshmallow as hard or soft?*

❺ Help the students record their observations in the "After" section of their *Laboratory Notebook* (see example on following page).

❻ Have the students repeat this exercise with several other objects.

Example

(Answers may vary.)

Marshmallow

Before

white
cylinder
light
fluffy

After

sticky
smashed
white

II. Think About It

Read the questions with your students.

❶ Using questions like the following, help the students think about their experiment and any observations they might have made about the objects they squeezed.

- *How did the objects feel in your hands? Were some objects heavy? Some light?*
- *Have the students discuss the size, shape, and color of the different objects.*
- *Were some objects difficult to hold? Did all the objects fit in your hand? Were some too large to hold?*

❷ Have the students discuss how difficult or easy it was to squeeze the objects.

❸ Help the students create a summary of their observations. There are two columns in the *Laboratory Notebook* — one labeled "Easy to Squeeze" and the other labeled "Hard to Squeeze." These are very general categories but will give the students a way to sort the different objects.

❹-❺ Review the chapter in the *Student Textbook* with the students and go over the summary statements. Have the students recall that work is what happens when a force moves an object, changes its shape, or changes how fast or slowly an object is moving.

Help them make the following connections.

1. *Their hand uses energy (from their body) in order to squeeze the object.*
2. *When squeezing the object, their hand generates a force on the object.*
3. *The object either changes shape as the force is applied or does not change shape.*
4. *The amount of work done is related to how much the object changes shape. The more the object changes shape, the more work is done.*

Help the students determine when they did the most work by squeezing the objects with their hands. Without telling them the answer, again remind them that the amount of work that is done depends on the amount the object changes shape. This means that even if they squeeze an object with all their effort, using lots of energy and applying lots of force, if the object does not change shape, they do no work.

Have the students circle the object they believe had the most work done to it when it was squeezed.

Have the students put a rectangle around the object they believe had the least work done to it when it was squeezed.

III. What Did You Discover?

Read the questions with your students.

❶-❺ The questions can be answered verbally or in writing. With these questions, help the students think about their observations. There are no right answers to these questions, and it is important for the students to write down or discuss what they actually observed. Help them explore how the answer they got may be different from what they thought might happen. If they guessed that more force would equal more work, they may be surprised to discover that this is not necessarily true.

IV. Why?

Read this section of the *Laboratory Notebook* with your students.

Discuss with the students how their body can be used as a tool to measure force and energy. Because their hands have nerve endings, they can sense the hardness or softness of different objects. Also, they can observe their muscles and breath as they squeeze different objects. This gives them an idea of how much energy is needed to generate different forces. The harder they squeeze an object, the more force they are generating.

Discuss with the students that the use of more force and more energy does not necessarily mean they did more work. The shape of an object has to change before work is done. If a force is applied, say to a rock, but the shape of the object does not change, no work is done. Discuss how it may feel as if they did work, but without an observable outcome, no work was done.

V. Just For Fun

Read this section of the *Laboratory Notebook* with your students.

Without a pair of pliers, it would be difficult for most young students to squeeze a tennis ball. However, with a pair of pliers it becomes much easier. The pliers are a form of tool called a lever, and the pliers actually multiply the amount of force exerted on the tennis ball. That is, with a little applied force on one end (the handle) there is much greater force applied at the other end (the tennis ball).

Experiment 4

Moving Energy in a Toy Car

Materials Needed

- toy car
- stiff cardboard or board (approximately .3 meter wide x 1 meter long [1 foot x 3 feet])
- several marshmallows

Optional
(see *Just For Fun* section)

- pennies
- tape

Objectives

In this experiment students will explore how one form of energy can be converted to another form of energy. They will observe the conversion of gravitational stored energy into kinetic energy.

The objectives of this lesson are to have students:

- Observe how one form of energy is converted to another form of energy.
- Learn how to collect data and create a table of their results.

Experiment

I. Observe It

Students will perform a simple experiment to explore the conversion of gravitational stored energy to kinetic energy. By using a toy car, they will observe how increasing the gravitational stored energy in the car will give it more kinetic energy (moving energy).

Read this section of the *Laboratory Notebook* with your students.

❶ Have the students place the board or cardboard sheet on the ground with the toy car at one end.

❷ Even though the car is not moving, have them write or draw their observations. You can explain to the students that this is the "starting point" in the experiment. Even though nothing is happening, scientists always record their observations at a starting, or reference, point. A starting, or reference point, gives scientists an observation with which to compare observations that follow.

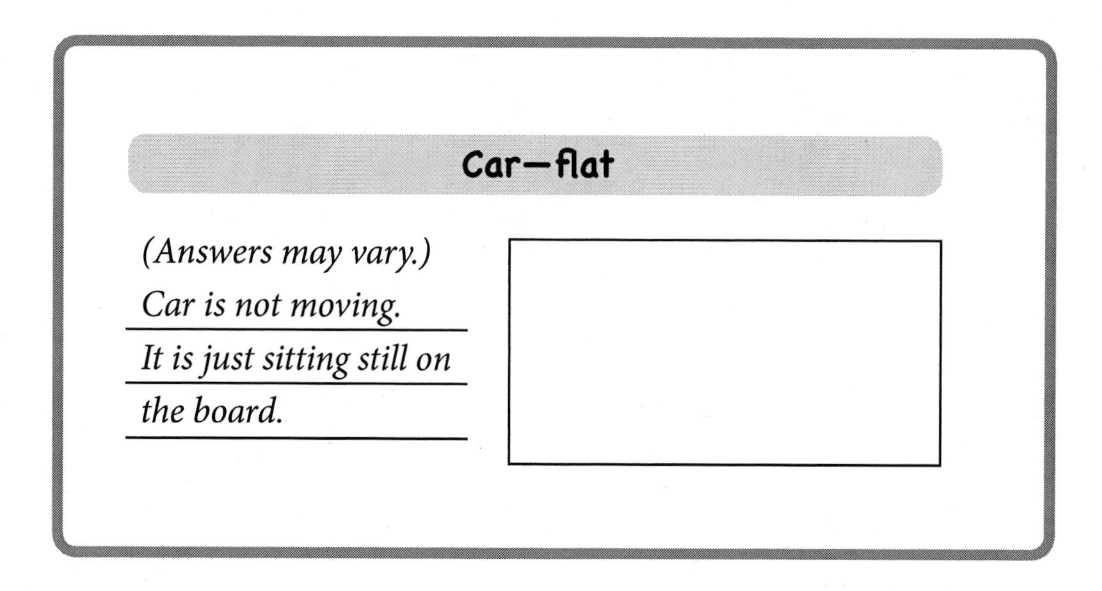

❸ Have the students stand at the end of the cardboard sheet or board on which the toy car is placed. Make sure the toy car is facing toward the other end of the cardboard sheet or board. Have the students lift the cardboard sheet or board to the level of their ankles, making a ramp. The toy car may or may not move at this height.

❹ Have the students record their observations. Guide their observations with the following questions:

- *When it starts out, is the toy car higher or lower now that you have lifted the board to your ankles?*
- *Did the toy car move? If so how far?*
- *If the toy car moved, how fast or slowly did it move?*
- *If the toy car moved, did it make it all the way to other end of the ramp?*

Car lifted to ankles

(Answers may vary.)
Car moved slightly
down the ramp. Only
an inch or so. It did
not move very fast.

❺-❿ Repeat Steps ❸-❹ of the experiment for the car lifted to the knees, then the hips, and then the chest.

Collect Your Results

Have the students summarize their results in the table provided.

II. Think About It

Read this section of the *Laboratory Notebook* with your students.

❶ Help the students think about their experiment and any observations they made about the toy car and its movement. The following questions may be used to guide discussion:

- *Did the toy car move easily once the board was lifted?*
- *Were the wheels sticky, or did they turn easily?*
- *Do you think the car was heavy enough to move down the board?*
- *Was the car made of plastic or metal?*
- *Do you think what the car was made of would make a difference in the results?*
- *Was the board or cardboard sheet smooth or rough?*
- *Do you think what the board was made of made a difference in your experiment?*

❷ Review with the students the discussion of gravitational stored energy in the *Student Textbook*. Any object that is elevated from the ground has some amount of gravitational stored energy. When the object falls to the ground, the gravitational stored energy is converted to kinetic energy. Objects that are higher than other objects have more gravitational stored energy.

❸ Have the students guess which car height had the least amount of gravitational stored energy and which height had the greatest amount of gravitational stored energy.

❹ The car had the least amount of gravitational stored energy when it was sitting flat on the ground. It had zero gravitational stored energy because it was at ground level. Have the students put a circle around this item.

❺ The car had the greatest amount of gravitational stored energy when it was lifted to the chest. Have the students draw a rectangle around this item.

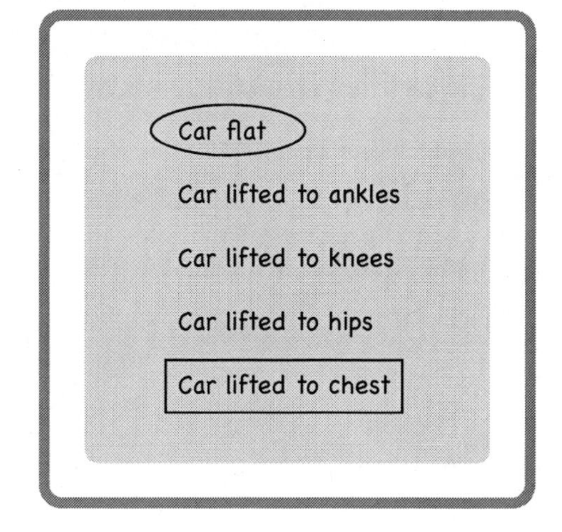

III. What Did You Discover?

Read the questions with your students.

❶-❺ The questions can be answered verbally or in writing. With these questions help the students think about their observations. There are no "right" answers to these questions, and it is important for the students to write or discuss what they actually observed.

Help the students explore how the answers they got may be different from what they thought might happen. Help them understand the concept of converting gravitational stored energy to kinetic energy. The more gravitational stored energy the car has, the more kinetic energy it will generate as it moves down the ramp.

IV. Why?

Read this section of the *Laboratory Notebook* with your students.

Discuss with the students how the toy car was able to move once it was lifted from the ground. Help the students understand that as their body lifted the ramp, the car gained gravitational stored energy by being moved to a greater height. Help the students see that as they lifted the toy car higher, they added more gravitational stored energy to the car.

V. Just For Fun

Read this section of the *Laboratory Notebook* with your students.

Have the students observe how kinetic energy can do work. As they raise the ramp and the toy car moves, the toy car's gravitational stored energy is converted to kinetic energy. Work is done as the car moves and as the marshmallow is smashed.

Help the students qualitatively determine how much kinetic energy is needed to smash a marshmallow. They may have to lift the car and ramp higher than their heads. Also, it is possible that no matter how high they lift the ramp, the marshmallow won't smash. If this happens, you can ask them what they think might happen if they used a heavier car or taped some pennies to the car they are using to make it heavier.

Have the students test one change to the experiment at a time so they can tell which change brought about a different result.

Have them record their results in the box provided.

Experiment 5

Playing With Physics

Materials Needed

- 2 marbles
- 3 playing cards
- shallow jar top
- vinegar
- baking soda
- measuring spoons

Suggested

- dominoes
- blocks
- electric car
- electric train
- marshmallow
- tongue depressor
- steel ball
- other objects chosen by the student

Objectives

In this experiment students will set up several series of experimental events to explore how energy is converted from one form to another.

The objectives of this lesson are to have students:

- Combine several experiments into a series.
- Observe how energy is converted from one form to another form.

Experiment

I. Observe It

In this section students will use two marbles to design a simple experiment to explore kinetic energy.

❶ Have the students place one marble on the floor. Have them sit some distance away from the stationary marble and roll a second marble into it.

❷ Help the students draw what happens to both marbles. If the marbles are of equal size, the first marble will likely stop, and the second marble will begin to roll when the first marble hits it. The kinetic energy of the first marble is converted into kinetic energy in the second marble.

❸ Have the students arrange three playing cards to make a small card house. The students may need some help stacking the cards.

❹ Have the students roll a marble, hitting the card house. Have them draw what happens to both the card house and the marble. The cards should fall down, and the marble will likely stop.

❺ Have the students fill a shallow jar top (such as one from a pickle jar) with vinegar.

❻-❼ Have the students add 15 ml (1 tablespoon) of baking soda to the vinegar and have them draw what happens. They should observe bubbles being released from the chemical reaction.

❽-❾ Have the students rinse out the jar top and refill it with vinegar. Then have them make a card house above the jar top and place 15 ml (1 tablespoon) of baking soda on top of the card house. Next, they will tip the card house with their fingers until the baking soda falls into the vinegar. Have them record their observations.

⑩ Now have the students assemble all of these steps into a short series. Their setup should look something like this:

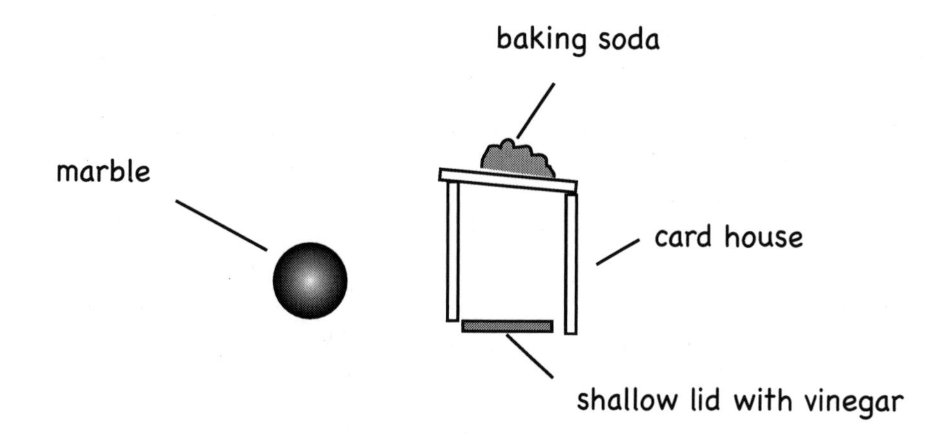

Have the students roll a second marble into the marble that is sitting close to the card house. This should cause the marble near the card house to roll into it and knock it down, causing the baking soda to fall into the shallow lid that contains the vinegar, resulting in a chemical reaction.

Have the students record their observations.

II. Think About It

❶ Help the students think about the different types of energy they used in this short series of smaller experiments. You can help them think about energy with the following questions.

- *Kinetic energy is the energy of something moving. What was moving in the experiment with two marbles?*
- *What was moving in the second experiment with a card house and a marble?*
- *Did anything move when you added vinegar to baking soda?*
- *What type of energy do you think is used when vinegar is combined with baking soda?*

❷ Review the *Energy to Energy* section in the *Student Textbook*. Have the students think about how energy is converted from one form to another as shown in the illustration given in the book. Explain how energy is never created or destroyed, just converted from one form to another.

❸ Have the students list the type of energy they think the object started with and the type of energy they think it was converted into. Have them fill out the chart using the energy labels given.

Object	Started With	Converted To
marble-->marble	*kinetic energy (rolling) marble*	*kinetic energy (rolling) marble*
marble-->card house	*kinetic energy (rolling)*	*kinetic energy (falling)*
card house upright--> card house falling	*stored energy (gravitational)*	*kinetic energy (falling)*
baking soda or vinegar -->baking soda + vinegar	*stored energy (chemical)*	*chemical energy*

III. What Did You Discover?

The questions can be answered verbally or in writing. With these questions, help the students think about their observations. There are no "right" answers to these questions, and it is important for the students to write or discuss what they actually observed. Help them explore how the answers they got may be different from what they thought might happen.

Help the students answer the questions about what happened to the energy at each stage of the series of experiments. Have the students think about what might have happened to all the energy at the end of the experiment. Where did it go?

IV. Why?

In this experiment students explored how energy is converted from one form to another. The students observed how the kinetic energy of one marble is converted into the kinetic energy of another marble. The students also observed how kinetic energy (rolling) was converted into kinetic energy (falling) and how chemical stored energy was converted into chemical energy.

Help the students understand that in each instance energy was converted from one form to another and was neither created nor destroyed. Help the students think through the last question. What happened to all the energy at the end of the experiment? There was no more kinetic energy, everything had stopped. There was no more gravitational stored energy, the cards had fallen. There was no more chemical stored energy or chemical energy once the reaction was complete. What happened to the energy? It was converted into a form of energy that is hard to convert — like heat energy. The heat energy was released into the air.

V. Just For Fun

Allow the students to explore the use of different materials to perform individual energy experiments and then connecting the small experiments as steps in a series. Help them make observations about the conversion of energy from one form to another. Have them record their results.

Some ideas are provided in the *Laboratory Notebook*.

Experiment 6

Rolling Marbles

Materials Needed

- 1 small glass marble
- 1 large glass marble

Objectives

In this experiment students will explore inertia, mass, and friction.

The objectives of this lesson are for students to:

- Observe how mass and inertia are related and how the force of friction slows and eventually stops kinetic (moving) energy.
- Learn how to collect data and create a table of their results.

Experiment

I. Observe It

Read this section of the *Laboratory Notebook* with your students.

In this experiment students will perform a simple experiment to explore inertia, mass, and friction. The students will use two types of marbles — a small glass marble and a large glass marble (a marble that is several times larger than the small marble).

❶ Have the students take the small glass marble and the large glass marble and roll them on a smooth surface.

❷ Have the students observe how each marble rolls. Guide their inquiry with the following questions:

- *Do the marbles go straight?*
- *How far do the marbles go?*
- *Where do the marbles stop?*
- *How do the marbles stop?*

❸ Have the students record their observations. An example follows.

Small and Large Marbles Rolling on Smooth Surface

(Answers may vary.)

The small marble rolled across the wood floor from the chair to the couch. It stopped when it hit the couch, and it bounced back and stopped a few inches from the couch.

Have the students draw what they observed.

4. Have the students take the same marbles and roll them across a carpeted surface or a grass lawn. This "rough" surface has more friction than a smooth surface.

5. Again help the students think about their observations. Guide their inquiry with the following questions:

- *Do the marbles roll straight?*
- *How far do the marbles go?*
- *Does one marble go farther than the other?*
- *How do the marbles stop?*
- *Is one marble harder to roll than the other?*

6. In the space provided, have the students record their observations. Have them pay particular attention to whether or not rolling the marbles on a rough surface is different from rolling them on a smooth surface. An example follows.

Small and Large Marbles Rolling on Rough Surface

(Answers may vary.)

The marble rolled across the carpeted floor from the desk to the chair. It did not roll as far as before. The marble just stopped on the carpet and did not hit anything. It was harder to roll the marble.

Have the students draw what they observed.

II. Think About It

Read this section of the *Laboratory Notebook* with your students.

❶ Review with the students the chapter *When Things Move* in the *Student Textbook,* which covers mass, inertia, and friction. Help the students understand that friction is a force that stops moving objects. Have them apply this idea to the experiment they just performed to show which surface has more friction. Also help the students connect the concepts of mass and inertia — the more mass, the more inertia.

Help the students think about their experiment and any observations they made about the two marbles rolling. You can use the following questions to guide the discussion:

- *Based on your observations, was one marble easier to roll on the smooth surface?*
- *Based on your observations, was one marble easier to roll on the rough surface?*
- *Did one marble go farther than the other marble on the smooth surface?*
- *Did one marble go farther than the other marble on the rough surface?*
- *Once the marbles were moving, did one marble move faster or slower than the other marble?*

❷ Help the students decide which surface has more friction. If the students are not sure, review their results with them. Show them that the marbles had much more difficulty rolling on the rough surface than on the smooth surface and that this tells the students that the rough surface has more friction. They will place a circle around **Rough Surface.**

❸ Help the students decide which marble has the most mass. If the students are unsure, have them hold one marble in each hand. Can they feel which marble is heavier? The heavier marble has the most mass. The larger marble will be heavier than the smaller marble, so it has more mass. They will place a box around **Large Marble**.

❹ Help the students decide which marble has the most inertia. The marble with the most mass has the most inertia. Since the large marble has the most mass, it also has the most inertia. They will place a triangle around **Large Marble**.

III. What Did You Discover?

Read this section of the *Laboratory Notebook* with your students.

The questions can be answered verbally or in writing. With these questions help the students think about their observations. There are no "right" answers to these questions, and it is important for the students to write or discuss what they actually observed. Help them explore how the answer they got may be different from what they thought might happen.

Help the students compare the two marbles, and help them explore any similarities or differences between how the two marbles rolled on the different surfaces. They should have discovered that the larger marble is slightly harder to start rolling than the smaller marble, but that once it is going, it is harder to stop (it rolls farther, or takes more force to stop it from rolling). In their discussions, help them use the words "friction," "inertia," and "mass." For example, they might say that the small marble has less mass and less inertia than the large marble.

IV. Why?

Read this section of the *Laboratory Notebook* with your students.

The students compared two marbles of different sizes and how they roll on two different surfaces. They may have observed the larger marble rolling farther on the rough surface than the smaller marble. They may also have observed that the larger marble can roll farther than the small marble on the smooth surface. However, it may have taken a bigger push to get the larger marble to roll. Explain to them that what they observed is related to mass, inertia, and friction. The larger marble has more mass and more inertia, and so in order to stop, it requires more friction than the smaller marble requires. Also explain to the students that because of its inertia, a marble in outer space could keep moving without ever stopping because there is no air friction in outer space to stop it.

V. Just For Fun

Have the students observe what happens when a small marble hits a large marble and when a large marble hits a small marble. Ask them to observe if there is any difference, and if so, why. Have the students record their observations.

Experiment 7

Speed It Up!

Materials Needed

- stopwatch or clock
- an area to run in
- items for marking the beginning and ending of the running distance

Objectives

In this experiment, students will explore how to calculate speed using basic tools.

The objectives of this lesson are for students to:

- Use suitable tools, techniques, and quantitative measurements when appropriate.
- Use a simple tool to make measurements.

Experiment

I. Think About It

Read this section of the *Laboratory Notebook* with your students.

Have the students think about different distances they might run. If running is not possible for the students, explore other ways they can measure distance traveled over time. They could measure a rolling ball or how fast a pet can run a certain distance.

Explore open inquiry with questions such as the following:

- *Do you think you can run the length of the yard?*
- *Do you think you can run the length of the block?*
- *Do you think you can run the length of the football stadium?*
- *Do you think you can run the length of the city?*

Help the students think about distance, how far they might be able to run, and that shorter distances will be easier to run than longer distances. Help them pick a distance to run that is suitable for them. Again, if running is not possible, then have them select a different object they can measure, such as a rolling ball, a baseball being thrown, a bowling ball, how fast a pet runs, or how fast a parent, friend, or teacher can run.

II. Observe It

Read this section of the *Laboratory Notebook* with your students.

Help the students mark a distance they can run. Have them use their feet as the measuring tool by walking heel-to-toe and counting the steps. Explain that this won't be an accurate measurement but rather an estimation. "Experiencing" the length of a distance by using their own feet gives them a sense of space that using a ruler or measuring tape would not.

Have the student run the distance between the two points they mark. They can either hold the stopwatch or timer themselves, or you can time them. However, pick one method and stick to it for all five runs. Switching the way the time is measured can introduce error.

Help them record their results in the table provided.

Help the students calculate their average speed by adding all the speeds together and dividing by the number of runs (5 if they ran 5 times).

III. What Did You Discover?

Read this section of the *Laboratory Notebook* with your students.

❶-❻ Have the students answer the questions. These can be answered orally or in writing. There are no right answers and their answers will depend on what they actually observed.

IV. Why?

Read this section of the *Laboratory Notebook* with your students.

Discuss any questions that might come up.

V. Just For Fun

Read this section of the *Laboratory Notebook* with your students.

Have the students measure how fast you or a friend can run the same distance that was measured in the first part of the experiment for the same number of times. Have them use the timer or stopwatch to record the times in the chart provided. Then have them calculate the average speed and compare it to their own average.

Experiment 8

Keep the Train on Its Tracks!

Materials Needed

- 4 plastic or Styrofoam cups with the mouth larger than the base
- 2 long poles (dowels work well or any two long sticks that are the same thickness from end to end)
- tape
- a cylinder, 10-13 cm long (4-5 inches) [any cylindrical object, such as a pencil, a dowel, a cylindrical block, or a cylindrical drinking glass that is not tapered; a paper towel tube may be used if it is filled with sand and the ends taped]
- chalk

Objectives

In this experiment, students will explore how differential rotational motion keeps a train's wheels on the tracks.

The objectives of this lesson are for students to:

- Describe the motion of an object by tracing its position over time.
- Observe how a change in diameter (size) changes the rotational motion of an object.

Experiment

I. Think About It

Read this section of the *Laboratory Notebook* with your students.

If you live near a train station it would be useful to look at the train wheels of a physical train. If not, do a library or internet search to study the physical shape of a train wheel.

Explore open inquiry with questions such as the following:

- *How is a train wheel shaped?*
- *How is a train wheel different from a bicycle or car wheel?*
- *How fast do trains travel?*
- *How do you think a train stays on the tracks when it travels fast?*

Have the students answer the questions in this section. There are no right answers.

II. Observe It

Read this section of the *Laboratory Notebook* with your students.

If possible, use a cement surface or solid, flat floor for doing this experiment.

❶-❷ Have the students roll first an un-tapered cylinder and then a tapered plastic or Styrofoam cup on a flat surface. Each time, have them trace the path of the object with a piece of chalk. Then, in the spaces provided, have them record their observations of how and how far the object rolls.

❸ Help the students tape the 2 poles to the ground parallel to each other and about 5 cm (2") apart. Make sure the track made by the poles is narrower than the length of the cylinder and the taped plastic cups.

❹ Have the students roll the cylinder on the poles. Have them observe how it moves and whether or not it stays on the poles or falls off. Have them record their observations in the space provided.

❺ Have the students take 2 plastic or Styrofoam cups, put the open ends together and tape them end-to-end.

❻ Have the students roll the taped plastic cups on the poles. Have them observe how they move and whether or not they stay on the poles or fall off. Have them record their observations in the space provided.

III. What Did You Discover?

Read this section of the *Laboratory Notebook* with your students.

❶-❸ Have the students answer the questions. These can be answered orally or in writing. Again, there are no right answers and their answers will depend on what they actually observed.

IV. Why?

Read this section of the *Laboratory Notebook* with your students.

Discuss any questions that might come up.

V. Just For Fun

Read this section of the *Laboratory Notebook* with your students.

❶ Have the students think about what would happen if they reversed the position of the cups and taped the bottoms (smaller ends) together, then rolled them on the poles. Have them record their ideas in the space provided. There are no right answers.

❷ Now the students will tape together the bottoms of two plastic cups and repeat the experiment. Have them record their results based on their observations.

Experiment 9

Lemon Energy

Materials Needed

- 3-5 large lemons
- knife
- 3-5 copper pennies older than 1982
- 3-5 galvanized (zinc coated) nails
- LED (recommended: 20mA 2 pin LED bulb, any color)*
- 4-6 pairs alligator clips (duct tape can be substituted for alligator clips)
- plastic coated copper wire, .6-1.2 m (2-4 feet)
- wire clippers
- small Phillips screwdriver

* A browser search can be used to look for an electronic parts store in your area. Or you can search on "20mA LED bulb 2 pin" to find an online supplier.

The LED bulb should look something like the above. One with flexible wire pins may be easier to use.

Objectives

In this experiment students will explore the concept of stored chemical energy by making a battery from lemons.

The objectives of this lesson are to have students:

- Observe how the stored chemical energy in a lemon can power a small LED.
- Summarize their observations.

Experiment

I. Observe It

Read this section of the *Laboratory Notebook* with your students.

Assembling the Three-Lemon Battery Electric Circuit

❶ Help the students make two slits in each lemon to insert a penny and a galvanized (zinc coated) nail. Make sure the slits go past the lemon rind and into the fleshy part of the lemon. Have the students place a penny in one slit and a zinc nail in the other slit of each lemon. These are the battery "leads."

❷ Using the wire clippers, cut a piece of coated copper wire 15-20 cm (6-8 inches) in length, and strip off about 1.5 cm (one-half inch) of plastic coating from each end. Using the Phillips screwdriver, attach a red alligator clip to one end of the wire and a black alligator clip to the other end. Now connect the red alligator clip to the penny of one lemon (the positive lead) and the black alligator clip to the zinc nail of a second lemon (the negative lead). Repeat, connecting the third lemon. If you don't have alligator clips, you can use duct tape but it may not stick very well.

You should now have a series of lemons connected by wires with alternating penny and zinc leads. The ends of the two lemons on the outside of the series will have one end of a wire attached and one end free.

❸ The LED will be connected to the remaining unattached alligator clips or wire ends.

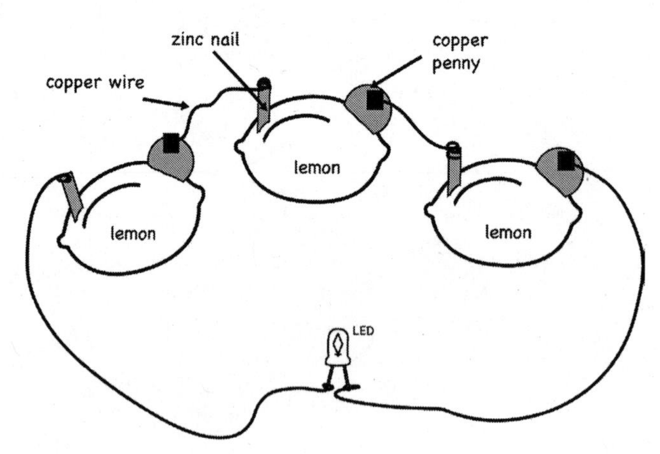

❹ When the students connect the LED to the free alligator clips or wires, the LED should light up. The light may be weak, so you may have to dim the room lights.

If the LED does not light up:

> Try switching the wire connections to the LED. It has positive and negative leads, and they may have been hooked up backwards. If the pennies are dull, clean them with a mild abrasive. Also, check the connections for all the pennies and zinc nails. Make sure all connections are secure, metal is touching metal, and the pennies and zinc nails are deep enough in the lemon to contact the fleshy part of the fruit. If the LED still won't light, try adding one or two more lemons to the circuit.

Use questions such as the following to help students make their observations.

- *Can you see any light coming from the LED?*
- *Are all the wires securely attached?*
- *Are the pennies and zinc nails in the soft part of the lemon?*

❺ Have the students record their observations in the space provided. They can write a description and/or draw a picture.

❻ Have the students remove one of the wires attached to one of the pennies. Guide their observations with questions such as the following:

- *Can you see any light coming from the LED?*
- *Reattach the wire. Does the light come back on?*
- *Remove the wire again. Does the light go off?*

❼ Have the students record their observations in the space provided. They can write a description and/or draw a picture.

❽-❾ Have the students reattach the wire to the penny and repeat steps ❻-❼, this time disconnecting a wire attached to a zinc nail. Use the same questions as in Step ❻.

In the chart provided, have the students summarize their observations. The expected results are as follows.

Summarize Your Observations

Trial	What Happened?
All Wires Connected	*The LED was illuminated*
Penny Wire Disconnected	*The LED was not illuminated*
Zinc Wire Disconnected	*The LED was not illuminated*

II. Think About It

❶ Have the students think about their experiment and make any observations about the lemon battery circuit that seem important to them. Use questions such as the following to help them think about the experiment.

- *How easy or difficult was it to set up the lemon battery circuit?*
- *How bright was the LED when all the wires were connected?*
- *How did the LED respond when you removed one of the copper wires from either the penny or the zinc nail?*

❷ Have the students review the chapter *Energy of Atoms and Molecules* in the textbook, which covers batteries and chemical energy. Discuss the concept that chemical reactions can produce electrical energy inside batteries. Help them relate this fact to the lemon battery.

❸ Have the students decide which statement is true. They should circle the statement "The LED will light up only when all the wires are connected."

❹ Have the students discuss any problems they may have encountered while doing the experiment. Some possible problems are:

- *Dull pennies (if the pennies are dull, there is an oxide layer on the outside of the metal which will prevent electrical contact).*
- *Lemon rinds that are too thick or too thin.*
- *Wires falling off.*

- *Tape not sticking.*
- *LED is defective.*
- *Too few lemons.*

Have a discussion with the students about how problems occur while doing experiments and that this is a normal part of doing science. Have the students discuss possible ways to fix the problems they encountered.

III. What Did You Discover?

Read this section of the *Laboratory Notebook* with your students.

With these questions, help the students think about their observations. There are no "right" answers to these questions, and it is important for students to write or discuss what they actually observed. Help them explore how the answers they got may be different from what they thought might happen.

Have the students compare what happened to the LED when all the wires were attached and what happened to the LED when they disconnected one or more of the wires.

IV. Why?

Read this section of the *Laboratory Notebook* with your students.

Have a discussion with the students about how they were able to use lemons as a battery. Also discuss with them how they created an electric circuit by connecting the lemon batteries together. In order to light an LED, at least three lemons are needed. Each lemon generates about 0.5 to 0.75 V of electric current, and an LED generally needs at least 2.0 V of electricity to illuminate. By combining the lemons together in a series, the voltage of each lemon is added to the others, and the total amount of electricity is enough to light the LED. Also discuss how when they disconnected one of the wires, the circuit was "broken," and the flow of electrons could no longer reach the LED.

V. Just For Fun

First, have the students make sure that all connections are secure, and then have them disconnect one of the wires from the LED. Have them hold the disconnected end of the LED wire in one hand and the end of the wire connected to a lemon in the other hand. Their body is now part of the electric circuit, conducting electricity and causing the LED to illuminate.

Experiment 10

Sticky Balloons

Materials Needed

- 2-3 rubber balloons
- string or thread, at least 2 meters (6 feet) cut in half
- scissors
- different materials to rub the balloon on, such as:
  - cotton clothing
  - silk clothing
  - wool clothing
  - wooden surface
  - plaster wall
  - metal surface
  - leather surface

Objectives

In this experiment students will explore static electricity and how charges can transfer from one object to another.

The objectives of this lesson are for students to:

- Observe how an object can become charged.
- Observe how a charged object can generate an attractive force.

Experiment

I. Observe It

Read this section of the *Laboratory Notebook* with your students.

In this section students will perform a simple experiment to explore the transfer of static electric charges. They will explore the concept that different kinds of materials and surfaces will donate electrons to a rubber balloon. Rubber has a greater attraction for electrons than some other materials, such as wool, hair, silk, or fur and so will become charged when rubbed against these materials.

❶ Have the students blow up a rubber balloon. They will need to securely tie the end. Have them place the balloon on a wall. The balloon should not be charged and, unless it has picked up charges from being handled, it will simply fall off the wall. This step is the "control."

❷ Have the students rub the balloon in their hair.

❸ Have them pull the balloon away from their hair and observe whether the balloon pulls their hair. If the balloon pulls their hair, it has attracted electrons from the hair and can be tested for an electric charge. If the balloon does not pull the hair, have the students rub the balloon in their hair again. In humid climates this experiment may not work very well since the moisture in the air prevents the charges from sticking to the balloon.

❹ Have the students "test" for the electric charge on the balloon by placing it on a wall.

❺ Help the students record their observations in the space provided. Use the following questions (also listed in the *Laboratory Notebook*) to guide their inquiry.

- *Does the balloon stick?*
- *How long does the balloon stick? 1 second? 2 seconds? 10 seconds? Longer than a minute?*
- *Does the balloon move around or stay still?*
- *What happens if you blow gently on the balloon? Does it stay stuck or does it fall off?*
  (The balloon should stick to the wall if there have been enough charges transferred from the hair to the balloon.)

Hair

(Example. Answers may vary.)

The balloon got really charged with my hair. It pulled my hair to the sides. The balloon really stuck to the wall, and even when I blew on the balloon it didn't move. It stayed on the wall longer than a minute.

Have the students draw what they observed.

❻ Have the students repeat Steps ❷-❺, rubbing the balloon on other materials. To discharge the balloon, wipe the outside of the balloon with a moist paper towel. Once the balloon is discharged, have the students rub the balloon against a different material or surface to recharge it. For each material have the students test the balloon to see how well it sticks to the wall. Have them record their observations, including how long the balloon stays on the wall each time.

II. Think About It

Read this section of the *Laboratory Notebook* with your students.

❶ Help the students think about their experiment and make any observations about the different materials they used to create charge on the balloon. You can use questions such as the following to guide the discussion:

- *Was it easy to get the balloon to carry a charge?*
- *What problems did you have in getting the balloon charged?*
- *Did some materials work better than other materials?*
- *How well did the balloon stick to the wall?*
- *Do you think using a wall to stick the balloon to is a good way to test for charge? Why or why not?*

❷ The chapter *Electricity* in the textbook covers electrons, charges, and force. Review this chapter with the students and help them understand that an electron carries a charge. The experimental results they observe are due to charges jumping from one object (hair, silk cloth, fur) to another object (the balloon).

❸ The wall test is used to determine how much charge the balloon collected from the various materials or surfaces. This is a qualitative estimation, and there may be some surfaces or materials that do not differ much from each other. You can help the students guess which materials may have had more charge by having them observe the length of time the balloon stayed on the wall. The longer the balloon stuck to the wall, the more charge it picked up from the material.

Have the students review their observations and create a chart listing the materials or surfaces used and how they affected the balloon from **Most Charge** to **Least Charge**.

III. What Did You Discover?

Read this section of the *Laboratory Notebook* with your students.

With these questions, help the students think about their observations. There are no "right" answers to these questions, and it is important for the students to write or discuss what they actually observed. Help them explore how the answer they got may be different from what they thought might happen.

Help the students explore how easy or difficult this experiment was to perform. Also, help them think about why they may get different results from the different materials used. Some materials may donate more charge to the balloon than other materials. The wall test is a way to determine how "much" charge the balloon collected. Help the students explore whether this is a good way to determine charge on the balloon. Ask the students if they can think of any other way to test the charges.

IV. Why?

Read this section of the *Laboratory Notebook* with your students.

Have a discussion about rubber being a material that easily picks up electrons from other surfaces. Discuss the "control" that was performed at the beginning of the experiment. By blowing up the balloon and applying it to the wall before they rubbed it in their hair, they got a feel for how the balloon behaves when it is uncharged.

Depending on the weather conditions in your hometown, this experiment was either easy to perform or did not work well. If the air is very dry, like in arid parts of the country, then static electric charges are easily created. If the air is more humid, then static charges are more difficult to create. Therefore, the results may vary depending on where you live.

V. Just For Fun

Have the students take two balloons and tie a piece of string or thread on one end of each balloon and then tie the other ends of the two pieces of string together.

Have the students drape the tied balloons over a shower rod, or help them fix the balloons to a doorway. Since the balloons are not charged, they should float free, touching each other but not touching any other surface.

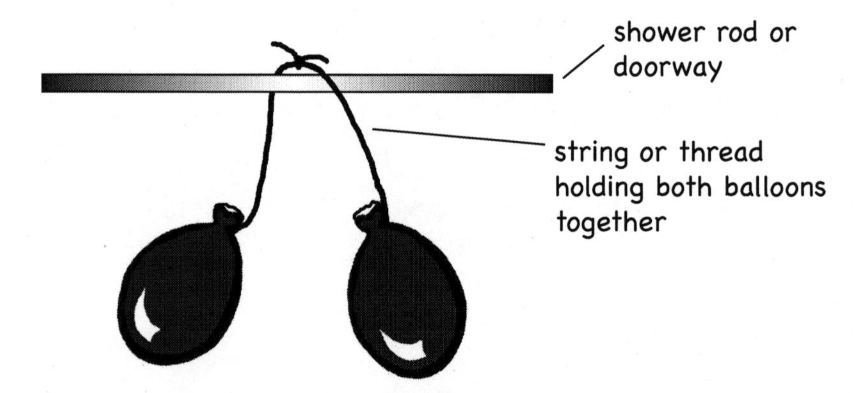

Help the students take the balloons and rub them in their hair. Have them gently let go of the balloons and watch what happens. If both balloons are charged, they will repel each other. Explain to the students that when things have the same kind of charge, they repel each other. When they have opposite charges, they attract each other.

Have the student record their results.

Experiment 11

Moving Electrons

Materials Needed

- lemon battery supplies
  (see *Lemon Energy* experiment)
- suggested test materials:
  Styrofoam
  plastic block
  cotton ball
  nickel coin
  metal paperclip
  plastic paperclip
- glass of water
- table salt, 15 ml (1 Tbsp.)

Objectives

In this experiment students will explore moving electric current and observe how insulating materials resist the flow of electrons through them.

The objectives of this lesson are to have students:

- Observe the effect of insulating materials on electric flow.
- Organize results in two different ways.

Experiment

I. Observe It

Read this section of the *Laboratory Notebook* with your students.

Students will perform a simple experiment to explore how different materials conduct electricity. They will test both metals and nonmetals and compare their results.

❶ Help the students assemble the lemon battery from the *Lemon Energy* experiment. Complete the setup exactly as in that experiment, and confirm that the LED is illuminated.

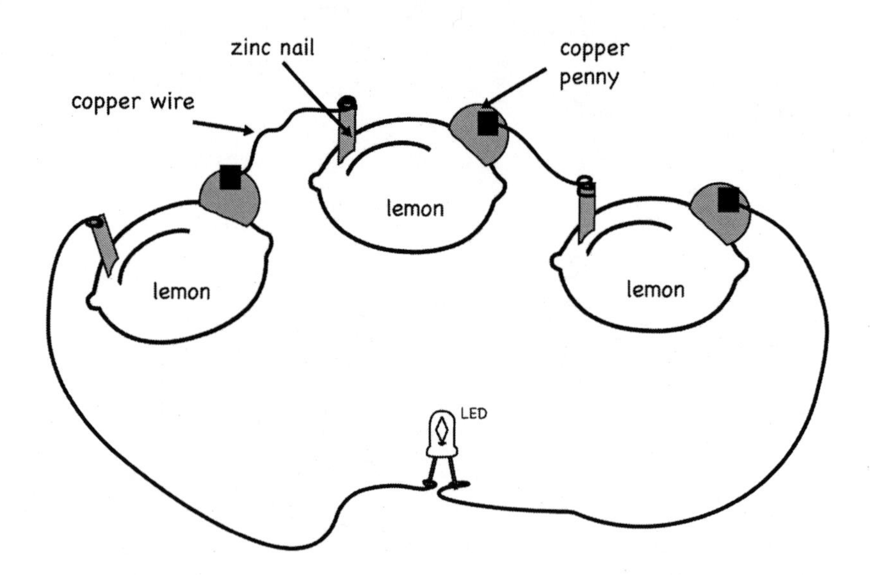

❷ Have the students cut one of the wires that connects two of the lemons. Tell them to observe the LED as they cut the wire.

❸ To reconnect the wire, help the students strip off about 1 cm (1/2 inch) of plastic coating from the ends of the cut wire. Have them reconnect the metal ends by briefly touching them together to make the LED illuminate, or they may want to twist the ends around each other. Make sure that metal is connected to metal and that a metal end has not been wrapped around the plastic coating. Have the students observe the LED and write and/or draw their observations in the space provided.

❹ Have the students disconnect the cut ends of the wire once again. Have them stick each metal end in a piece of Styrofoam. The ends should not touch each other, and the piece of Styrofoam will complete the connection. Have the students observe the LED and write and/or draw their observations.

❺ Have the students remove the Styrofoam and reconnect the wires as they did in Step ❸. Have them observe what happens to the LED and then write and/or draw their observations in the space provided.

❻ Have the students repeat Steps ❹-❺ using the other items on the materials list. If some of the materials are not available, other materials can be substituted. Have the students test a few insulators (plastics, cotton, wool, etc.) and a few conductors (metals).

❼ Have the students summarize their results in the table provided. If an item has been substituted, have them mark out the listed item and write in the new item. There should be a mixture of LED "ON" and LED "OFF" results as shown in the chart below.

Item	LED
Start—wires connected	*ON*
Wires apart	*OFF*
Wires connected	*ON*
Styrofoam	*OFF*
Wires connected	*ON*
Plastic block	*OFF*
Cotton Ball	*OFF*
Nickel coin	*ON*
Metal paperclip	*ON*
Plastic paperclip	*OFF*

II. Think About It

Read this section of the *Laboratory Notebook* with your students.

❶ Help the students think about their experiment and make any additional observations about the different materials they used to test the flow of electrons. Use questions such as the following to guide their inquiry.

- *Did you notice a difference in how the LED responded when different materials were used as part of the connection?*
- *What problems did you have connecting the wires to the different materials?*
- *Do you think some of the problems you had affected your results?*
- *Do you think the LED would light up if you used bigger (or smaller) pieces of plastic, Styrofoam, or cotton?*
- *Do you think the LED would be brighter if you used larger pieces of metal?*

❷ Review with the students the *Moving Electrons* chapter of the *Student Textbook*, which covers moving charges. Help the students understand that in order for electrons to flow through a material, the electrons have to be free to jump from one atom to the next. Have them think about the fact that insulators are insulators all the way down to their atoms and that using a larger piece of plastic or Styrofoam will not make an insulator conduct electricity.

❸ Have the students use the chart provided to organize the materials they tested. This exercise allows the students to explore alternative ways of examining scientific data. Explain to the students that scientists will often reorganize their data in ways that help them understand different aspects of the experiment. Here the students will see that those items that illuminated the LED are grouped together as conductors and those items that did not illuminate the LED are grouped together as insulators.

III. What Did You Discover?

Read this section of the *Laboratory Notebook* with your students.

Have the students think about their observations and then answer the questions. There are no "right" answers to these questions, and it is important for the students to write or discuss what they actually observed. Help them explore how the answer they got may be different from what they thought might happen.

Help the students examine the types of materials that illuminated or did not illuminate the LED. It will be clear from the data that plastics, Styrofoam, and cotton are like each other in that they are all materials that do not allow the flow of electrons (i.e., are insulators). It will also be clear from the data that coins, metal paperclips, and other metals do allow the flow of electrons (i.e., are conductors). Help the students use the language of "conductors" and "insulators" to formulate their answers.

IV. Why?

Read this section of the *Laboratory Notebook* with your students.

In this experiment students explored how conductors and insulators behave differently. Conductors, such as metals, allow electrons to flow and permit the illumination of the LED. Insulators do not allow electrons to flow and do not permit the illumination of the LED. Explain that the experiment they set up is a good way to determine which materials conduct electricity and which materials do not. Also explain that there are some materials that allow a restricted electron flow. These materials are called resistors.

V. Just For Fun

Have the students take the ends of the cut wire and place them in a glass of water. Depending on the type of tap water you are using, the LED may or may not illuminate.

Have the students add 15 ml (1 Tbsp.) of table salt to the water and stir until it is completely dissolved. The LED should now illuminate when the ends of the wires are placed in the saltwater.

Discuss with the students how this experiment showed that water and saltwater are conductors because they allow electrons to flow through them.

Experiment 12

Magnet Poles

Materials Needed

- two bar magnets with the poles labeled "N" and "S"

Objectives

In this experiment students will explore the nature of magnetic poles.

The objectives of this lesson are to have students:

- Observe how magnetic poles behave when placed close together.
- Make a scientific conclusion based on their observations.

Experiment

I. Observe It

Read this section of the *Laboratory Notebook* with your students.

In this section the students will perform a simple experiment to explore how magnetic poles attract and repel each other.

❶ Have the students place the bar magnets several inches apart on a table with the "N" on one magnet facing the "N" on the other. The magnets need to be far enough apart that there are no repulsive forces interacting.

❷ Have the students gently push the end of one magnet closer to the end of the other magnet. Have them go slowly so they can observe what happens with the stationary magnet. At some point the stationary magnet will change. It will move away from the magnet that is being pushed (the stationary magnet will be repelled). At this point don't discuss the "north" and "south" poles of the magnets, just focus the students' attention on observing what is happening to the magnets. Help them write and/or draw their observations in the space provided. This is *Trial 1*.

❸ Again have the students place the two magnets on the table several inches apart. Have them reverse the magnetic pole of one magnet by flipping the magnet over so the "S" pole of this magnet is facing the "N" pole of the other magnet.

❹ Have the students gently push the magnets together as they did in Step ❷. This time the magnets should be attracted to each other and may even snap together. This is *Trial 2*.

❺ Have the students repeat Steps ❶-❹ several times.

Help the students make observations for each trial. Guide inquiry with questions such as the following:

- *How close can you bring the magnets together before something changes?*
- *What happens when you bring the magnets together slowly?*
- *What happens when you bring the magnets together quickly?*
- *Do the magnets behave the same way each time you bring two "N"s together?*
- *Do the magnets behave the same way each time you bring an "N" and an "S" together?*

❻ Help the students summarize their results in the chart provided.

Trial	N-N or N-S	Together or Apart
Trial 1	*N-N*	*Apart*
Trial 2	*N-S*	*Together*
Trial 3	*N-N*	*Apart*
Trial 4	*N-S*	*Together*
Trial 5	*N-N*	*Apart*
Trial 6	*N-S*	*Together*
Trial 7	*N-N*	*Apart*
Trial 8	*N-S*	*Together*
Trial 9	*N-N*	*Apart*
Trial 10	*N-S*	*Together*

II. Think About It

Read this section of the *Laboratory Notebook* with your students.

❶ Help the students think about the magnets and the two different ways the magnets were positioned as they were pushed together.

❷ Review with the students *Magnets* chapter of the *Student Textbook,* which covers magnetic poles. Have a discussion about magnets having two opposite poles that are called "north" and "south." Have the students look at the magnets and observe the "N" and "S" letters.

❸ Have the students look at the results they gathered in the previous table. In this table they recorded N-N or N-S notations along with the observations they made of whether the magnets moved together or apart. Have the students cover up the column that has the N-N and N-S notations, and have them look only at the column that says whether or not the magnets moved together or apart. Using this information, have the students guess which trials had the "same" poles and which trials had the "opposite" poles, and have them record their answers in the table provided.

Trial	Same or Opposite
Trial 1	*Same*
Trial 2	*Opposite*
Trial 3	*Same*
Trial 4	*Opposite*
Trial 5	*Same*
Trial 6	*Opposite*
Trial 7	*Same*
Trial 8	*Opposite*
Trial 9	*Same*
Trial 10	*Opposite*

❹ Have the students uncover the hidden column and compare the two tables. Have them note whether or not their answers in the second table match the second column of the previous table.

In this exercise they are using their scientific results to make a guess, predicting which poles were the same and which were opposite based only on their observations.

III. What Did You Discover?

Read this section of the *Laboratory Notebook* with your students.

With these questions, help the students think about their observations. There are no "right" answers to these questions, and it is important for the students to write or discuss what they actually observed. Help them explore how the answer they got may be different from what they thought might happen.

Help the students summarize their results. Have them discuss what happened when they pushed the two "N" poles together and when they pushed the "N" and "S" poles together. Ask them if, based on this experiment, they could take two magnets that were not labeled "N" and "S" and predict which poles were the same and which were opposite. Help them understand that they do not need to know "N" and "S" but only "same" and "opposite." Remind them that opposite poles attract and similar poles repel and that they can predict which poles are the same or opposite by whether or not the magnets are attracting each other or repelling each other.

IV. Why?

Read this section of the *Laboratory Notebook* with your students.

In this experiment students explored the magnetic poles of magnets. These poles interact and produce either an attractive or repulsive force. The students took two magnets, and by bringing the ends of the magnets together they explored how the poles interact with each other.

The students also did several "trials" to explore the magnetic poles. By repeating the steps of the experiment several times, the students could "play" with how the magnets interact with each other, making observations for each trial. Scientists generally do more than one trial when they are conducting experiments. By playing with the experiments, scientists discover things that they might have missed if they only did the experiment once.

V. Just For Fun

Have the students test the magnets with different household items. Have them touch a magnet to a number of different objects, both metal and nonmetal, to find out which materials will interact with the magnet.

Have them record their results in the table provided.

More REAL SCIENCE-4-KIDS Books
by Rebecca W. Keller, PhD

Building Blocks Series
yearlong study program — each Student Textbook has accompanying Laboratory Notebook, Teacher's Manual, Lesson Plan, Study Notebook, Quizzes, and Graphics Package

Exploring Science Book K (Activity Book)
Exploring Science Book 1
Exploring Science Book 2
Exploring Science Book 3
Exploring Science Book 4
Exploring Science Book 5
Exploring Science Book 6
Exploring Science Book 7
Exploring Science Book 8

Focus On Series
unit study program — each title has a Student Textbook with accompanying Laboratory Notebook, Teacher's Manual, Lesson Plan, Study Notebook, Quizzes, and Graphics Package

Focus On Elementary Chemistry
Focus On Elementary Biology
Focus On Elementary Physics
Focus On Elementary Geology
Focus On Elementary Astronomy

Focus On Middle School Chemistry
Focus On Middle School Biology
Focus On Middle School Physics
Focus On Middle School Geology
Focus On Middle School Astronomy

Focus On High School Chemistry

Super Simple Science Experiments

21 Super Simple Chemistry Experiments
21 Super Simple Biology Experiments
21 Super Simple Physics Experiments
21 Super Simple Geology Experiments
21 Super Simple Astronomy Experiments
101 Super Simple Science Experiments

Note: A few titles may still be in production.

Gravitas Publications Inc.
www.gravitaspublications.com
www.realscience4kids.com